How I Wonder Where You Are

L.I.F.E.* Adventures Book Two

*Love Inspires Families Everywhere: Stories about adoption,
foster care, stepchildren, and all blended families

Written by **Anna Maria DiDio**

illustrated by **Tatiana Lobanova**

ALL AGES

Love At The Border Publishing, Philadelphia, PA

First print edition 2022.

Published in the United States of America.

Summary: Carla, who is adopted from Colombia, wonders about her birth mother and family roots when she is asked by her teacher to create a family tree as part of a school assignment.

Cover design and illustrations by Tatiana Lobanova

ISBN (paperback) 978-1-7377035-2-5

For more information, visit the author's website: amdidio.com

L.I.F.E. Adventures
Love Inspires Families Everywhere

A Letter to Parents

How I Wonder Where You Are is book TWO in the series of L.I.F.E. Adventures – stories about adoption, foster care, stepchildren, and all blended families.

Every adopted child experiences a special type of grief related to traumatic separation from the birth mother. *Disenfranchised grief*, also called hidden grief, is minimized by society and not openly acknowledged. Even within a loving family environment there is still pain about the family that is unknown. Where did I come from? Who do I look like? Birthdays and school assignments related to culture or a family tree can be triggering. Adoptees test boundaries while fearing disapproval or abandonment by the adoptive family.

Notes on Disenfranchised Grief: Top Five Reminders for Parents

1. Every adoption or foster journey is unique. Consider what your child has lost: family, culture, friends, smells, food, caregivers.
2. Reassure your child by being patient and sensitive, acknowledging the emotions and behaviors exhibited due to disenfranchised grief: crying, anger, aggression, making up stories and difficulty with relationships.
3. Work through the pain. Grief is a complex emotion. Talk it out, cry it out, reach out to professionals. Share their "adoption story" early and often with NO secrets.
4. Be there for your child during triggering school assignments about culture and/or a family tree. Include a photo or tree "decorations" valued as uniquely personal.
5. Accept that grief and "wondering" will happen even when the adoption experience is positive and loving.

*Visit **amdidio.com** to find free resources for your adoption journey, including an audible excerpt from my memoir **Love at the Border, An Adoption Adventure**.*

For my family...

We looked at lots of family pictures together.
There are so many people I don't know...

"Look at Aunt Mary's freckles, they look just
like Sarah's and yours too, mom."

I don't look like my parents or sound like them because I was adopted from Colombia.

Sarah is my sister. Sometimes I am jealous of her. I wish someone would say *Oh, you look so much like your mom.* People say that to Sarah all the time.

When we are out shopping I see women who look like me and wonder...*maybe she could be my first mom.* But I know she lives in a different country.

I wonder...*what does my first mom look like?*
Sometimes I dream about her.

I am happy for my new family but still miss the food where I lived before.

Sometimes my mom doesn't know what to cook for me.

It's fun to help my mom in the kitchen!

I wonder...*what kind of food does my first mom make at home?*

It has been so difficult to learn English and
sometimes my brain and tongue don't match.

I like teaching my family Spanish words. Last night they all took turns learning how to say *jamón*.

One of the most important things that I brought with me from Colombia is my birthday. It makes me think about my first mom.

I wonder...*what does she sound like?*
Does she think about me on this day?

To celebrate my birthday, Mom, Dad, Sarah, and I went to the movies. We ate popcorn and candy.

I feel like I want to cry but I don't.

Our family tree is really big. Today I met Aunt Mary, Uncle Bobby, and my cousins.

Then I met Aunt Kathy. She's from California
and was holding a teddy bear dressed in
the colors of the Colombian flag.

She asked me about my favorite food
and I told her: *"Empanadas!"*

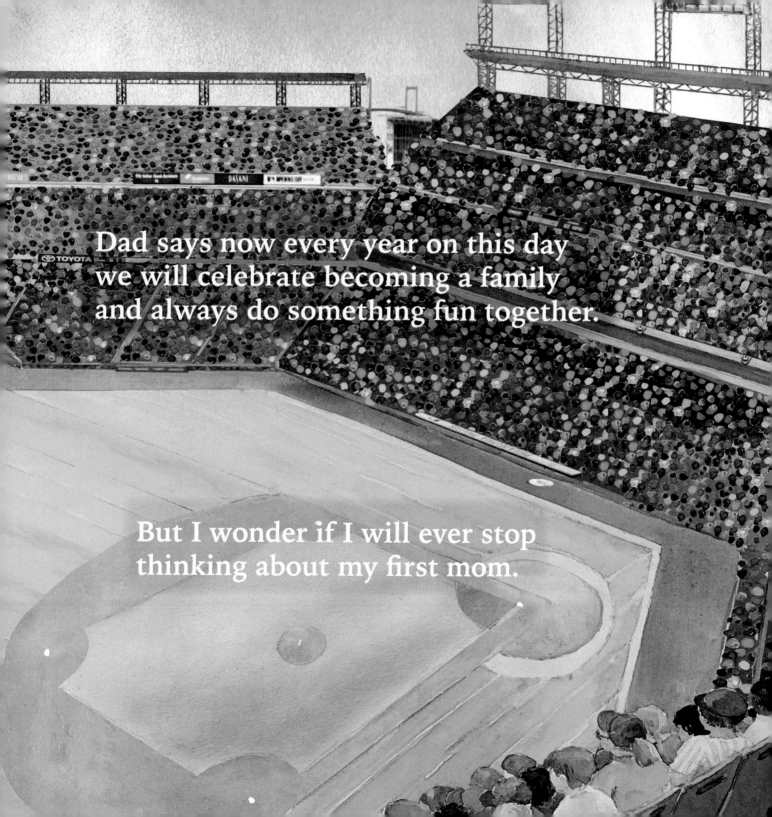

Dad says now every year on this day we will celebrate becoming a family and always do something fun together.

But I wonder if I will ever stop thinking about my first mom.

My mom, dad, and Sarah love me, and every day I am learning to love them back.

Wondering is just a part of me now.

When I wonder, I
think of my favorite
nursery rhyme —

Twinkle Twinkle, I've come so far,
How I wonder where you are.
In the world, all around I see,
I am learning to love

Mom,

Dad,

Sarah,

...and me!

About the Author

Anna Maria DiDio, MSW an adoptive mother, was inspired to write her memoir, *Love at the Border, An Adoption Adventure* after her own family journey. Now her L.I.F.E.* Adventures children's books feature stories about adoption, foster care, stepchildren, and all blended families from the point of view of the child. Anna Maria hopes that her books encourage open and honest exploration about what children are thinking and feeling within their own unique families. She can be found at home in Philadelphia walking everywhere, swimming laps, reading biographies, or baking chocolate chip cookies except when traveling to new and exciting places with her husband Richard.

Love Inspires Families Everywhere

About the Illustrator

Tatiana Lobanova was born in Moscow, Russia, and discovered a love of drawing as a young girl. "Tanya" trained in art school and also theatre college. Upon graduation, she worked within the theatrical community as an artist and stage designer, constantly perfecting her technique for illustration and classical painting. Tanya currently works full-time as a freelance illustrator. Tanya loves gardening and amateur ballet and lives in The Hague, the Netherlands with her husband Andrey and two children.

Thank you for reading my book.
Don't forget to leave a review!

Every review is precious to me. I appreciate your feedback and need your input to make the next book better.

Please take a few minutes to let me know your thoughts.

Thank you!
Anna Maria DiDio

*Visit **amdidio.com** to find free resources for your adoption journey, including an audible excerpt from my memoir **Love at the Border, An Adoption Adventure**.*